g
h
i
j
k
l
m
u
v
w
x
y
z

Dear Parent,

The My First Steps to Reading® *series is based on a teaching activity that helps children learn to recognize letters and their sounds. The use of predictable language patterns and repetition of familiar words will also help your child build a basic sight vocabulary. Your child will enjoy watching the characters in the books place imaginative objects in "letter boxes." You and your child can even create and fill your own letter box, using stuffed animals, cut-out pictures, or other objects beginning with the same letter. The things you can do together are limited only by your imagination. Learning letters will be fun—the first important step on the road to reading.*

The Editors

 Published by Scholastic Inc., 90 Old Sherman Turnpike, Danbury, Connecticut 06810, by arrangement with The Child's World, Inc.
Scholastic offers a varied selection of children's book racks and tote bags. For details about ordering, please write to: Scholastic At Home, 90 Old Sherman Turnpike, Danbury, CT 06810, Attention: Premium Department

Originally published as *My "First" Sound Box* by The Child's World, Inc.

My First Steps to Reading is a registered trademark of Grolier Publishing Co. Inc.
SCHOLASTIC and associated logos are trademarks and/or registered trademarks of Scholastic Inc.

ISBN 0-7172-6549-8

Printed in the U.S.A.

My First Book

Jane Belk Moncure
illustrated by Colin King

eyes

nose

mouth

hair

feet

toes

hug

friends

balloons

hats

pillows

bed

cup

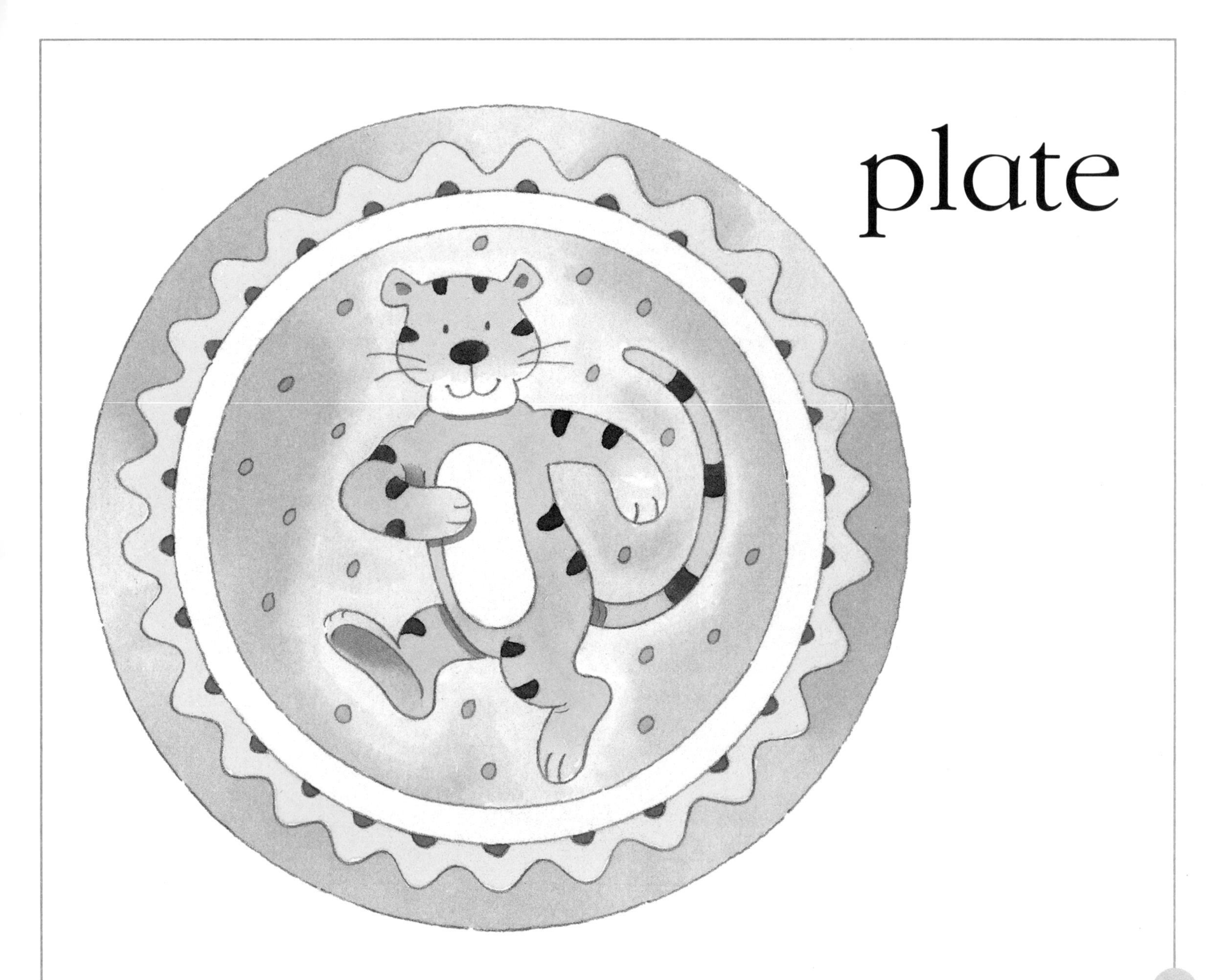

plate

apple

cake

ball

bicycle

bear

doll

bunny

blocks

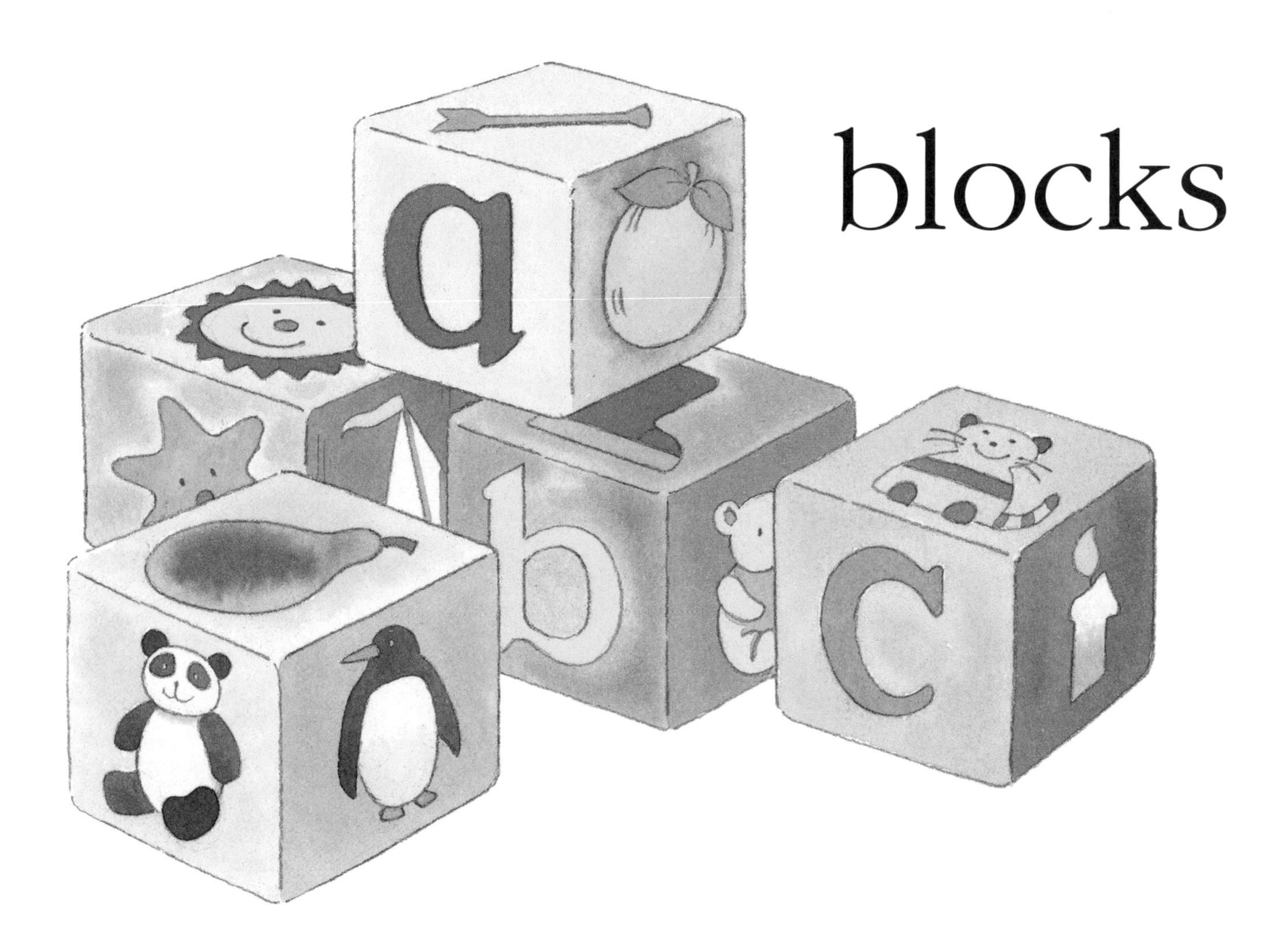

box

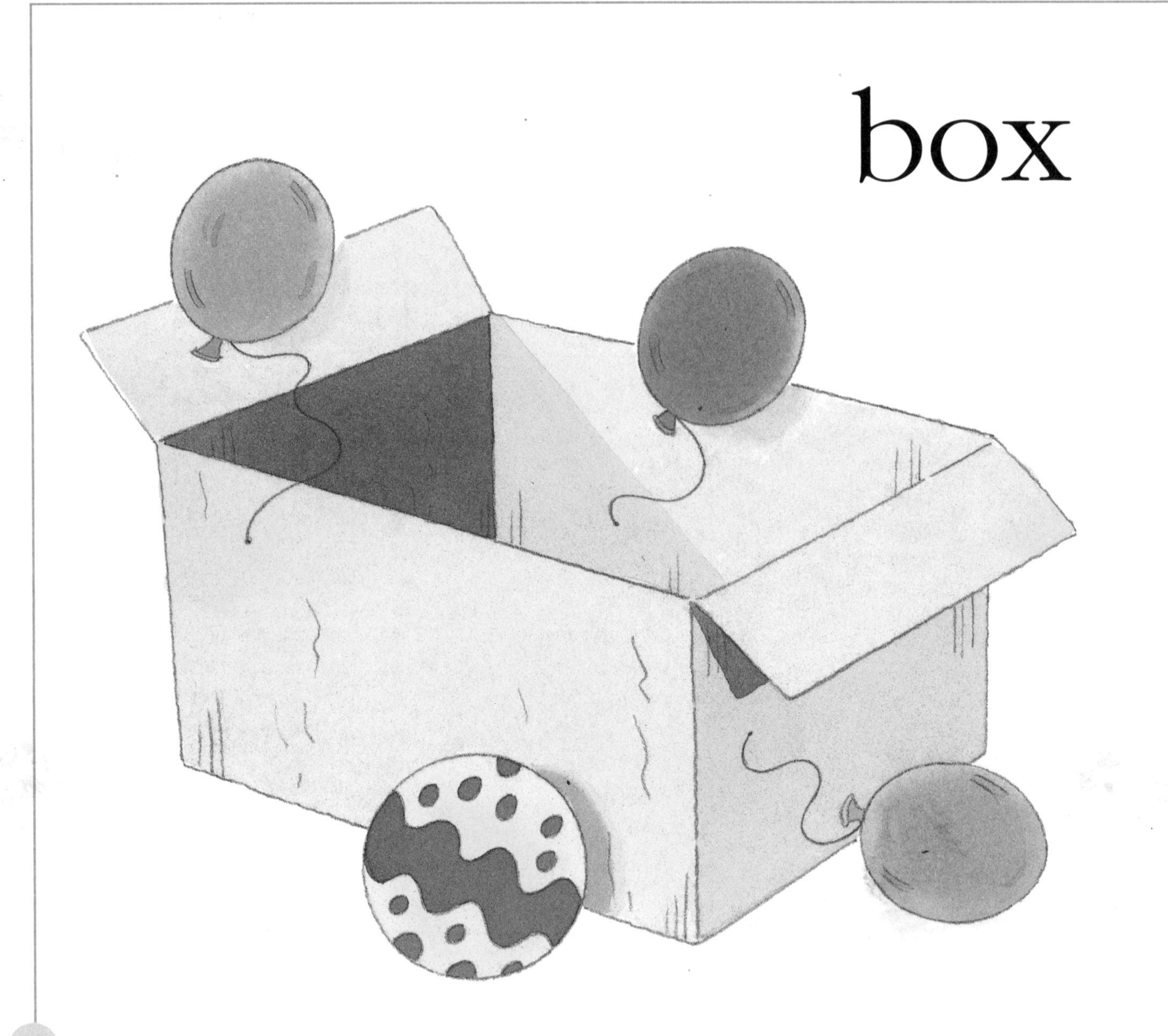

I will fill my box.

Aa
Bb
Cc
Dd
Ee
Ff
Nn
Oo
Pp
Qq
Rr
Ss
Tt
A B C
My First
Steps to
READING®